The Communication Skills Workbook

Self-Assessments, Exercises & Educational Handouts

Ester A. Leutenberg
John J. Liptak, EdD

Illustrated by
Amy L. Brodsky, LISW

Duluth, Minnesota

Whole Person Associates
101 West 2nd St., Suite 203
Duluth MN 55802

800-247-6789

books@wholeperson.com
www.wholeperson.com

The Communication Skills Workbook
Self-Assessments, Exercises & Educational Handouts

Printed in the United States of America

10 9 8 7 6 5 4 3 2 1

Editorial Director: Carlene Sippola
Art Director: Joy Morgan Dey

Library of Congress Control Number: 2007942421
ISBN: 978-1-57025-226-6

Using This Book *(For the professional)*

Interpersonal communication is the process of sending and receiving messages with another person. This process sounds and appears to be easy. However, in reality, communication involves a very complex set of skills, as complex as those necessary for driving a car or reading a map. Part of the reason for this complexity is that messages can be communicated and received in a variety of ways, i.e. listening, speaking, signing, touch, eye contact. People need adequate communication skills in order to survive and thrive in our challenging society. Effective communication skills are critical in many walks of life including:

- Developing and maintaining friendships
- Participating in the community
- Being effective in educational settings
- Parenting successfully
- Finding a job
- Succeeding in the workplace
- Maintaining intimate relationships

As indicated from the list above, the better the communication skills, the more effective and successful people will be. The good news is that communication skills can be taught. Effective communication skills can be learned and improved through practice. Most people typically learn their communication skills from their family, teachers and friends. Problems arise when these influences are poor role models. When people learn ineffective communication skills it is important for them to identify their areas of weakness, learn more effective ways of communicating with other people, and find ways to practice these critical skills.

Over the last century many different workbooks, workshops, and self-help systems have been designed to help people explore communication issues and blocks to effective communication. In the past twenty years, many research studies have focused on the value of self-reflection and journaling as a way of exploring personal characteristics, identifying ineffective behaviors, and examining thoughts and feelings that lead to ineffective behaviors. This book is unique because it combines two powerful psychological tools designed to enhance communication skills: self-assessment and journaling.

The Communication Skills Workbook contains five separate sections. In each, the participants will learn more about themselves as well as the impact of effective and ineffective communication skills:

- Active Listening Scale helps individuals determine how effectively they listen when communicating.
- Nonverbal Communications Scale helps individuals examine how their body language is affecting their interpersonal communications.
- Communications Skills Scale helps individuals measure how effective they are at using communication skills to initiate, build and maintain interpersonal relationships.
- Social Radar Scale helps individuals explore how attuned they are to verbal and nonverbal cues.
- Negotiation Skills Scale helps individuals explore how well they negotiate to get what they want without manipulating or alienating other people.

These sections serve as avenues for individual self-reflection, as well as group experiences revolving around identified topics of importance. Each assessment includes directions for easy administration, scoring and interpretation. In addition, each section includes exploratory activities, reflective journaling activities and educational handouts to help participants discover their habitual, ineffective methods of communicating with others and to explore new ways for enhancing interpersonal communication.

Using This Book *(continued)*

The art of self-reflection goes back many centuries and is rooted in many of the world's greatest spiritual and philosophical traditions. Socrates, the ancient Greek philosopher, was known to walk the streets engaging the people he met in philosophical reflection and dialogue. He felt that this type of activity was so important in life that he went so far as to proclaim, "The unexamined life is not worth living." The unexamined life is one in which the same routine is continually repeated without ever thinking about its meaning to one's life or and how this life could be lived. However, a structured reflection and examination of beliefs, assumptions, characteristics and patterns can provide a better understanding, which can lead to a more satisfying life. A greater level of self-understanding about important life skills is often necessary to make positive, self-directed changes in the negative patterns that keep repeating throughout life. The assessments and exercises in this book can help promote this self-understanding. Through involvement in the in-depth activities, the participant claims ownership in the development of positive patterns.

Journaling is an extremely powerful tool for enhancing self-discovery, learning, transcending traditional problems, breaking ineffective life and career habits, and helping to heal from psychological traumas of the past. From a physical point of view, writing reduces stress and lowers muscle tension, blood pressure and heart rate levels. Psychologically, writing reduces sadness, depression and general anxiety, and leads to a greater level of life satisfaction and optimism. Behaviorally, writing leads to enhanced social skills, emotional intelligence and creativity.

By combining reflective assessment and journaling, your participants will be exposed to a revolutionary method for enhancing critical communication skills.

Preparation for using the assessments and activities in this book is important. The authors suggest that prior to administering any of the assessments in this book, you complete them yourself. This will familiarize you with the format of the assessments, the scoring directions, the interpretation guides and the journaling activities. Although the assessments are designed to be self-administered, scored and interpreted, it helps for facilitators to be prepared to answer questions about the assessments for participants.

For example, the following statement is included on the Communications Skills Scale:

#25. *I use "I" statements to deliver criticism to others.*

Some of your participants might not understand "I statements." With your background and experience, as well as familiarity with the tests, you should be able to clarify for participants any confusing words or phrases.

Thanks to the following professionals whose input in this book has been invaluable!

Rondi Atkin, MFA

Nancy Day, OT Reg (Ont.)

Kathy Khalsa, OTR/L

Kathy Liptak, Ed.D.

Eileen Regen, M.Ed., CJE

Lucy Ritzic, OTR/L

Karal Stern, LISW, LICDC

The Assessments, Journaling Activities, and Educational Handouts

Materials in the Assessment, Journaling Activity, and Educational Handout sections in this book are reproducible and can be photocopied for participants' use. The assessments contained in this book focus on self-reported data and thus are similar to ones used by psychologists, counselors, therapists and career consultants. To receive accurate and useful information, participants need to respond honestly. By being honest, participants help themselves to learn about the unproductive and ineffective patterns in their lives, and to uncover information that might be keeping them from being as successful as they might be.

An assessment instrument can provide participants with valuable information about themselves; however, these assessments cannot measure or identify everything. The assessments' purpose is not to pigeon-hole certain characteristics, but rather to allow them to explore all of their characteristics. This book contains self-assessments, not tests. Tests measure knowledge or whether something is right or wrong. These assessments provide information about a topic of importance in the participant's education, life and career communications. There are no right or wrong answers.

When administering the assessments in this workbook, remember that the items are generically written so that they will be applicable to a wide variety of people but will not account for every possible variable for every person. The assessments are not specifically tailored to one person. Use them to help participants identify negative themes in their lives and to find ways to break the hold that these patterns and their effects have in their life.

Advise the participants taking the assessments that they should not spend too much time trying to analyze the content of the questions; their initial response will most likely be true. Regardless of individual scores, encourage participants to talk about their findings and their feelings pertaining to what have they discovered about themselves. Talking about communication skills will certainly enrich their lives and the relationships in their lives.

Layout of the Book

The Communication Skills Workbook is designed to be used either independently or as part of an integrated curriculum. You may administer one of the assessments and the journaling exercises to an individual or a group with whom you are working, or you may administer a number of the assessments over one or more days.

This book includes five sections, each of which contains:

- **Assessment Instruments** — Self-assessment inventories with scoring directions and interpretation materials. Group facilitators can choose one or more of the activities relevant to their participants.
- **Activity Handouts** — Practical questions and activities that prompt self-reflection and promote self-understanding. These questions and activities foster introspection and promote pro-social behaviors.
- **Reflective Questions for Journaling** — Self-exploration activities and journaling exercises specific to each assessment to enhance self-discovery, learning, and healing.
- **Educational Handouts** — Handouts designed to enhance instruction can be used individually or in groups to enhance communication skills and to provide positive reinforcement for effective interpersonal skills. They can be distributed, converted into masters for overheads or transparencies, or written down on a board and discussed.

Who should use this program?

This book has been designed as a practical tool for helping professionals, such as therapists, counselors, psychologists, teachers, and group leaders. Depending on the role of the professional using *The Communication Skills Workbook* and the specific client or group's needs, these sections can be used individually, combined, or as part of an integrated curriculum for a more comprehensive approach.

Why use self-assessments?

Self-assessments are important in teaching various communication skills because they help participants to engage in these ways:

- Become aware of the primary motivators that guide their behavior
- Explore and learn to *let go* of troublesome habits and behavioral patterns learned in childhood
- Explore the effects of unconscious childhood messages
- Gain insight and *a wake up call* for behavioral change
- Focus their thinking on behavioral goals for change
- Uncover resources they possess that can help them to cope better with problems and difficulties
- Explore their personal characteristics without judgment
- Develop full awareness of their strengths and weaknesses

Because the assessments are presented in a straightforward and easy-to-use format, individuals can self-administer, score and interpret each assessment at their own pace.

Introduction for the Participant

It is very important for our physical and psychological well-being that we maintain interpersonal relationships with other people in our life. These relationships are a necessity, not a luxury, and we need to be prepared in order to develop and maintain these critical relationships. Positive, supportive relationships can help us cope with difficult times in our lives, reduce psychological distress, and increase our general happiness and life satisfaction. Communication can literally be described as the center of all interpersonal relationships. The problem is that communication can be very difficult to initiate, so that one can develop and maintain positive relationships with other people. Managing the dynamics of personal relationships can be quite challenging.

Communication is definitely a skill that takes considerable learning and practice to gain a sense of mastery. Personal relationships are at times difficult to maintain because they are extremely complex, constantly changing and very fragile. That is why it is beneficial to use effective communication skills in personal relationships. Effective communication skills ensure that we will listen actively to what the other person is saying, communicate clearly, negotiate to ensure *win-win* situations, maintain effective body language and be aware of the cognitive distortions that may block clear communication between two people.

The good news is that if you feel like you are not a good communicator, you can learn and practice the skills that will help your interpersonal relationships grow and work more effectively. This book relies on a self-reflective method that is both therapeutic and fun. *The Communication Skills Workbook* is designed to help you learn about all the various skills that can be used to enhance or block effective communication between you and other people.

TABLE OF CONTENTS

SECTION I – Active Listening

SECTION II – Nonverbal Communication

TABLE OF CONTENTS

SECTION I:

Active Listening Scale

Name____

Date______________________

Active Listening Scale Directions

Active listening is a critical component of any conversation you have with another person. The Active Listening Scale was designed to help you examine how effective you are in identifying, assessing and overcoming blocks to listening.

This assessment contains 32 statements. Read each of the statements and decide whether or not the statement describes you. If the statement describes you, circle the number next to that item under the **True** column. If the statement does not describe you, circle the number next to that item under the **False** column.

In the following example, the circled number under **False** indicates the statement is not true of the person completing the inventory.

	TRUE	FALSE
I try to understand what the other person is saying	2	(1)

This is not a test and there are no right or wrong answers. Do not spend too much time thinking about your answers. Your initial response will likely be the most true for you. Be sure to respond to every statement.

(Turn to the next page and begin)

Active Listening Scale

When I am talking with another person . . .

	TRUE	FALSE
1. I try to understand what the other person is saying	2	1
2. I am constantly comparing myself to the other person	1	2
3. I try to read the other person's mind	1	2
4. I put aside my judgments of the person	2	1
5. I listen for feelings as well as content	2	1
6. I ask for clarification if I do not understand something	2	1
7. I constantly disagree with the other person	1	2
8. I agree with what the other person says, even if I don't	1	2
9. I go to great lengths to prove I am right	1	2
10. I make appropriate eye contact	2	1
11. I hear what I want to hear	1	2
12. I mentally plan my response while the other person is talking	1	2
13. I often paraphrase what the other person says	2	1
14. I listen with my full attention	2	1
15. I don't worry about the other person's feelings	1	2
16. I often find myself lying	1	2

TOTAL = _______

(Continued on the next page)

(Active Listening continued)

When I am talking with another person . . .

	TRUE	FALSE
17. I attempt to understand the underlying meaning of the words	2	1
18. I finish the other person's sentences	1	2
19. I think about other things while the person is talking	1	2
20. I jump in and give advice before the person stops talking	1	2
21. I start making jokes	1	2
22. I ask questions to get further information	2	1
23. I judge the person ahead of time	1	2
24. I reassure and support the other person	2	1
25. I try to solve the other person's problems for them	1	2
26. I am easily distracted	1	2
27. I focus on specific points and shut out the rest of the message	1	2
28. I am attentive to that person's body language and tone of voice	2	1
29. I find myself daydreaming	1	2
30. I always seem to understand the other person's position clearly	2	1
31. I often interrupt the other person	1	2
32. I let the other person know I heard what was said	2	1

TOTAL = _______

(Go to the Scoring Directions on the next page)

Active Listening Scale Scoring Directions

The Active Listening Scale is designed to measure how proficient you are at listening to others with whom you are talking. For each of the items on the previous two pages, add the numbers that you circled and put that number in the TOTAL space at the bottom of each page.

Then, add the two numbers together and transfer your total to the space below:

ACTIVE LISTENING TOTAL = ________

Profile Interpretation

SCALE SCORE	INDICATIONS
56 – 64	You are an active listener. You go out of your way to truly hear what the other person is saying, ask questions for more information and paraphrase important points back to the communicator.
40 – 55	You are an average listener. You could use some help in further developing your listening skills.
32 –39	You need to further develop your listening skills.

Regardless of your score, the exercises and activities that follow are designed to help you increase your listening skills.

BUILDING YOUR LISTENING SKILLS

Actively listening to other people sounds easy, doesn't it? In reality, it is one of the most difficult aspects of effective communication. Active listening takes commitment and knowledge of barriers that are keeping you from listening effectively to others. The following exercises are designed to help you begin thinking about the potential blocks to active listening and take steps in listening effectiveness.

Blocks to Active Listening

I. DAYDREAMING

Daydreaming is allowing your attention to wander to other events or people. It is a time when you stop listening and drift away into your own fantasies.

In what situations do you find yourself daydreaming?

____

____

____

When you find yourself daydreaming, with whom are you talking?

____

____

____

When you find yourself daydreaming, what is the conversation about?

____

____

____

When you are daydreaming, how do you feel about the other person?

____

____

____

(Continued on the next page)

(Blocks to Active Listening continued)

II. REHEARSING

Rehearsing is when you are busy thinking about what you are going to say next, so that you never completely hear what the other person is telling you.

In what situations do you find yourself rehearsing?

___

___

___

When you find yourself rehearsing, with whom are you talking?

___

___

___

When you find yourself rehearsing, what is the conversation about?

___

___

___

When you are rehearsing, how do you feel about the other person?

___

___

___

(Continued on the next page)

(Blocks to Active Listening continued)

III. FILTERING

Filtering is when you listen to certain parts of the conversation, but not all.

In what situations do you find yourself filtering conversations?

___

___

___

When you find yourself filtering conversations, with whom are you talking?

___

___

___

When you find yourself filtering conversations, what is the conversation about?

___

___

___

When you are filtering conversations, how do you feel about the other person?

___

___

___

(Continued on the next page)

(Blocks to Active Listening continued)

IV. JUDGING

Judging is when you have stopped listening to the other person because you have already judged, placed labels, made assumptions about, or stereotyped the other person.

In what situations do you find yourself judging?

____

____

____

When you find yourself judging, with whom are you talking?

____

____

____

When you find yourself judging, what is the conversation about?

____

____

____

When you are judging, how do you feel about the other person?

____

____

____

(Continued on the next page)

(Blocks to Active Listening continued)

IV. DISTRACTIONS

Distraction occurs when your attention is divided by something internal to you (headaches, worry, hunger) or external to you (traffic, whispering, others talking).

In what situations do you find yourself distracted?

When you find yourself getting distracted, with whom are you talking?

When you find yourself getting distracted, what is the conversation about?

When you are distracted, how do you feel about the other person?

Mastery of Active Listening Skills

Listening is a critical aspect of effective communication. Regardless of your score, the following exercises will help you become a better listener. Try practicing all of the active listening skills that follow, then select and use the one with which you feel most comfortable.

PARAPHRASING

In paraphrasing, you restate, in your own words, what you think the other person just said.

You can use such phrases as "In other words..." or "What I am hearing you say is...."

In the following spaces, try to paraphrase what the speaker is saying.

What the speaker says	How you could paraphrase
"I think I am going to leave him."	*"What I hear you saying is that you are going to ask for a divorce!"*
"My partner never listens to me."	
"I desperately need a vacation."	
"I hate my job."	
"I can't decide if I should go to the party."	

(Mastery of Active Listening Skills continued)

REFLECTION OF FEELINGS

In reflection of feelings, you restate what the person has said to you much like paraphrasing. However, in this skill you restate what you think the speaker is feeling.

In the following spaces, try to reflect the feelings of the speaker.

What the speaker says	How you could reflect feelings
"I think I am going to leave him."	*"You sound very frustrated!"*
"My partner never listens to me."	
"I desperately need a vacation."	
"I hate my job."	
"I can't decide if I should go to the party."	

(Mastery of Active Listening Skills continued)

CLARIFICATION

In clarification, you tell the other person what you thought you heard, learn whether you were right or wrong, and then ask questions to clarify.

In the following spaces, try to clarify what the speaker is saying.

What the speaker says	How you could clarify what was said
"I think I am going to leave him."	*"You don't think it's worth staying to try and work things out. Is that accurate?"*
"My partner never listens to me."	
"I desperately need a vacation."	
"I hate my job."	
"I can't decide if I should go to the party."	

(Mastery of Active Listening Skills continued)

BODY LANGUAGE

Showing active listening through your body language conveys the message that you are interested and listening, encouraging the speaker to tell you more. Some suggestions for effective body language include the following:

- Maintain eye contact
- Move closer to the person, but do not cross over any personal boundaries
- Lean forward if you are sitting
- Nod from time-to-time
- Say things like "yes" or "uh huh"
- Keep your posture open to the person by keeping your arms unfolded and uncrossed
- Keep distractions to a minimum

When you are communicating with other people, which of the above body language cues do you maintain?

____

____

____

When you are communicating with other people, which of the above body language cues do you need to do more often?

____

____

____

Listening Strengths

What are your strengths when you listen to other people?

Listening Weaknesses

What are your weaknesses when you listen to other people?

Weak Listening Skills

If the use of weak listening skills negatively impacts your interactions with others, such as customers, teachers, strangers, relatives and friends, describe how.

Stages of Listening

- Hear a message from another person
- Make some meaning from the message
- Evaluate the message based on your needs and situation
- Respond to the message, either verbally or nonverbally

Improving Communication Skills

- Clarify
- Paraphrase
- Reflect Feelings
- Use Body Language
- Let other person talk
- Ask open-ended questions
- Provide feedback but do not interrupt
- Spend more time listening than talking
- Do not finish the other person's sentences
- Plan responses after the other person finishes speaking

Blocks to Active Listening

- Judging
- Filtering
- Rehearsing
- Daydreaming
- Preconceived ideas
- Thinking of oneself
- Perceptions of the person
- Distractions — internal or external
- Focus too much on facts, not ideas

SECTION II:

Nonverbal Communication Scale

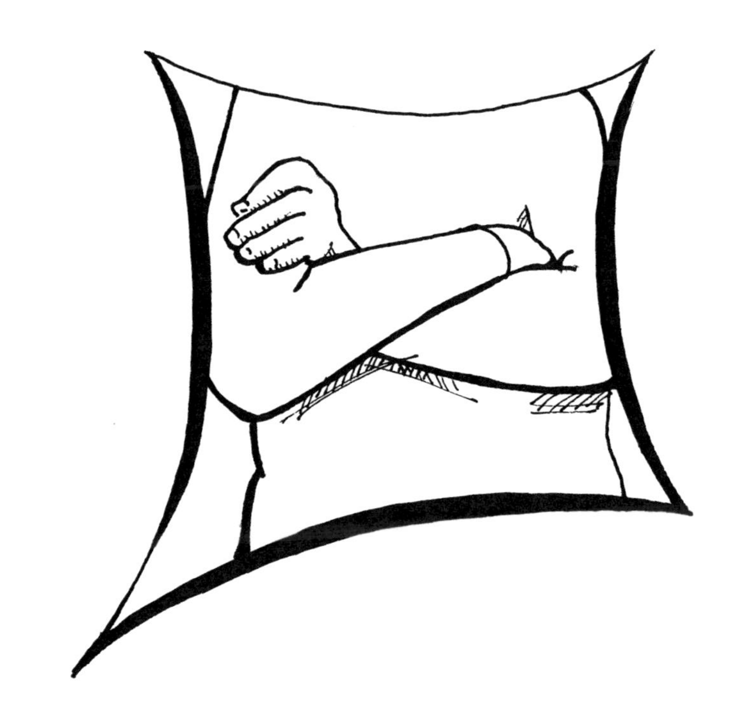

Name____

Date__________________________

Nonverbal Communication Scale Directions

Communication is the process of sending and receiving messages that allow people to share information, ideas and knowledge. Most people think about communication as speaking to someone, but communication actually has two components – verbal and nonverbal. Nonverbal communication can be defined as communication without words and includes such behaviors as facial expressions, touching, gestures, posture, body language and spatial distance between two people.

The Nonverbal Communication Scale can help you identify the ways that you communicate nonverbally. This scale contains four sections with sixteen statements in each section. Read each of the statements and decide if the statement is true or false. If it is true, circle the word TRUE next to the statement. If the statement is false, circle the word **False** next to the statement. Ignore the numbers after the **True** and **False** choices. They are for scoring purposes and will be used later. Finish all of the items before going back to score this scale.

In the following example, the circled **False** indicates that the item is false for the participant completing the scale:

SECTION I: IMMEDIATE FAMILY MEMBERS

When talking with immediate family members (spouse, children, partner, etc.), I . . .

1. maintain steady eye contact while speaking   True (1)   (False (0))

Score ______

This is not a test and there are no right or wrong answers. Do not spend too much time thinking about your answers. Your initial response will likely be the most true for you. Be sure to respond to every statement.

(Turn to the next page and begin)

Nonverbal Communication Scale
I – Immediate Family Members

When talking with immediate family members (spouse, children, partner, etc.), I . . .

1.	maintain steady eye contact while speaking	True (1)	False (0)	Score _____
2.	yawn or show other signs of boredom	True (0)	False (1)	Score _____
3.	exhibit a blank facial expression	True (0)	False (1)	Score _____
4.	always greet them warmly	True (1)	False (0)	Score _____
5.	nod my head a lot to confirm what the person is saying	True (1)	False (0)	Score _____
6.	often find myself turning my head away due to distractions	True (0)	False (1)	Score _____
7.	roll my eyes a lot	True (0)	False (1)	Score _____
8.	have a relaxed posture	True (1)	False (0)	Score _____
9.	often lean toward the other person to express interest	True (1)	False (0)	Score _____
10.	often cross my arms across my chest	True (0)	False (1)	Score _____
11.	rhythmically drum or tap my fingers	True (0)	False (1)	Score _____
12.	find myself clenching my fists	True (0)	False (1) 0	Score _____
13.	find myself looking at my watch or a clock	True (0)	False (1)	Score _____
14.	use a lot of hand gestures to make my point	True (1)	False (0)	Score _____
15.	stand tall and straight	True (1)	False (0)	Score _____
16.	make appropriate physical contact (pat on back, touch arm)	True (1)	False (0)	Score _____

TOTAL __________

(Continued on the next page)

(Nonverbal Communication Scale continued)

II – Family of Origin

When talking with members of my family of origin (siblings, parents, grandparents), I . . .

17. maintain steady, eye contact while speaking	True (1)	False (0)	Score _____
18. yawn or show other signs of boredom	True (0)	False (1)	Score _____
19. exhibit a blank facial expression	True (0)	False (1)	Score _____
20. always greet them warmly	True (1)	False (0)	Score _____
21. nod my head a lot to confirm what the person is saying	True (1)	False (0)	Score _____
22. often find myself turning my head away due to distractions	True (0)	False (1)	Score _____
23. roll my eyes a lot	True (0)	False (1)	Score _____
24. have a relaxed posture	True (1)	False (0)	Score _____
25. often lean toward the other person to express interest	True (1)	False (0)	Score _____
26. often cross my arms across my chest	True (0)	False (1)	Score _____
27. rhythmically drum or tap my fingers	True (0)	False (1)	Score _____
28. find myself clenching my fists	True (0)	False (1)	Score _____
29. find myself looking at my watch or a clock	True (0)	False (1)	Score _____
30. use a lot of hand gestures to make my point	True (1)	False (0)	Score _____
31. stand tall and straight	True (1)	False (0)	Score _____
32. make appropriate physical contact (pat on back, touch arm)	True (1)	False (0)	Score _____

TOTAL __________

(Continued on the next page)

(Nonverbal Communication Scale continued)

III – Community Members

When talking with members of my community (support group, house of worship, teachers, police officers, neighbors, etc.), I …

33. maintain steady eye contact while speaking	True (1)	False (0)	Score _____
34. yawn or show other signs of boredom	True (0)	False (1)	Score _____
35. exhibit a cold, blank facial expression	True (0)	False (1)	Score _____
36. always greet them warmly	True (1)	False (0)	Score _____
37. nod my head a lot to confirm what the person is saying	True (1)	False (0)	Score _____
38. often find myself turning my head away due to distractions	True (0)	False (1)	Score _____
39. roll my eyes a lot	True (0)	False (1)	Score _____
40. have a relaxed posture	True (1)	False (0)	Score _____
41. often lean toward the other person to express interest	True (1)	False (0)	Score _____
42. often cross my arms across my chest	True (0)	False (1)	Score _____
43. rhythmically drum or tap my fingers	True (0)	False (1)	Score _____
44. find myself clenching my fists	True (0)	False (1)	Score _____
45. find myself looking at my watch or a clock	True (0)	False (1)	Score _____
46. use a lot of hand gestures to make my point	True (1)	False (0)	Score _____
47. stand tall and straight	True (1)	False (0)	Score _____
48. make appropriate physical contact (pat on back, touch arm)	True (1)	False (0)	Score _____

TOTAL __________

(Continued on the next page)

(Nonverbal Communication Scale continued)

IV – Co-workers / Supervisor / Employees

When talking with co-workers, supervisor or employees, I . . .

49. maintain steady eye contact while speaking — True (1) False (0) Score ______
50. yawn or show other signs of boredom — True (0) False (1) Score ______
51. exhibit a cold, non-receptive facial expression — True (0) False (1) Score ______
52. always greet them warmly — True (1) False (0) Score ______
53. nod my head a lot to confirm what the person is saying — True (1) False (0) Score ______
54. often find myself turning my head away due to distractions — True (0) False (1) Score ______
55. roll my eyes a lot — True (0) False (1) Score ______
56. have a relaxed posture — True (1) False (0) Score ______
57. often lean toward the other person to express interest — True (1) False (0) Score ______
58. often cross my arms across my chest — True (0) False (1) Score ______
59. rhythmically drum or tap my fingers — True (0) False (1) Score ______
60. find myself clenching my fists — True (0) False (1) Score ______
61. find myself looking at my watch or a clock — True (0) False (1) Score ______
62. use a lot of hand gestures to make my point — True (1) False (0) Score ______
63. stand tall and straight — True (1) False (0) Score ______
64. make appropriate physical contact (pat on back, touch arm) — True (1) False (0) Score ______

TOTAL ___________

(Go to the Scoring Directions on the next page)

Nonverbal Communication Scale Scoring Directions

The Nonverbal Communication Scale is designed to help you identify how you communicate through your body language in a variety of social situations. To score this scale, you need to determine your scores on each of the individual scales and for the overall nonverbal communication total.

To score the scale, look at the sixty-four items you just completed. Now you need to focus on numbers after each choice rather than the TRUE or FALSE. Total your score for each section.

Use the spaces below to transfer your scores to each of the scales below. Then total the scores and put that number in the TOTAL column.

I. Immedite Family Members Scale — Total Score from #1 through #16 = ________

II. Family of Origin Scale — Total Score from #17 through #32 = ________

III. Community Members Scale — Total Score from #33 through #48 = ________

IV. Co - Workers/Supervisor/Employees Scale — Total Score from #49 through #64 = ________

TOTAL of all FOUR SCALES ________

Profile Interpretation

Individual Scale Score	Total Score All 4 Scales	Result	Indications
0 – 5	0 – 21	Low	You show poor body language when communicating with other people. Most of the time you do not maintain good posture, you rarely use effective facial espressions, you often fail to keep an effective distance when communicating and do not maintain effective eye contact.
6 – 10	22 – 42	Moderate	You show good body language when communicating with other people. Most of the time you maintain posture, use effective facial espressions, keep an effective distance when communicating and maintain effective eye contact.
11 – 16	43 – 64	High	You exhibit very good body language when communicating with other people. You effectively maintain posture, use effective facial espressions, keep an effective distance when communicating and maintain effective eye contact.

The higher your score on the Nonverbal Communication Scale, the more apt you are to show effective nonverbal communication when talking with other people. In the areas in which you score in the **Moderate** or **Low** range you should make efforts to use better nonverbal communication skills when speaking with people in that aspect of your life.

No matter if you scored **Low**, **Moderate** or **High**, the exercises and activities that follow are designed to help you explore your nonverbal communication skills in various roles you play in life.

Exploring Nonverbal Communication
with

Your Immediate Family Members

Complete the following questions about how you show nonverbal communication with members of your family. When you have answered all of the questions, look for self-defeating nonverbal communication patterns that keep recurring in your life.

1) How has your nonverbal communication enhanced your relationships with family members?

____

____

____

2) How has your nonverbal communication hurt your relationships with family members?

____

____

____

3) How has your nonverbal communication been misinterpreted by members of your family?

____

____

____

4) Does the nonverbal communication you exhibit with members of your family show how you are truly feeling at the time?

____

____

____

Exploring Nonverbal Communication
with

Your Family of Origin

Complete the following questions about how you show nonverbal communication with members of your family of origin. When you have answered all of the questions, look for self-defeating nonverbal communication patterns that keep recurring in your life.

1) How has your nonverbal communication enhanced your relationships with members of your family of origin?

____

____

____

2) How has your nonverbal communication hurt your relationships with members of your family of origin?

____

____

____

3) How has your nonverbal communication been misinterpreted by members of your family of origin?

____

____

____

4) Does the nonverbal communication you exhibit with members of your family of origin show how you are truly feeling at the time?

____

____

____

Exploring Nonverbal Communication
with

Your Community Members

Complete the following questions about how you show nonverbal communication with members of your community. When you have answered all of the questions, look for self-defeating nonverbal communication patterns that keep recurring in your life.

1) How has your nonverbal communication enhanced your relationships with members of your community?

____

____

____

2) How has your nonverbal communication hurt your relationships with members of your community?

____

____

____

3) How has your nonverbal communication been misinterpreted by members of your community?

____

____

____

4) Does the nonverbal communication you exhibit with members of your community show how you are truly feeling at the time?

____

____

____

Exploring Nonverbal Communication with

Your Co-workers / Supervisors / Employees

Complete the following questions about how you show nonverbal communication with co-workers, supervisors and employees you have at work. When you have answered all of the questions, look for self-defeating nonverbal communication patterns that keep recurring in your life.

1) How has your nonverbal communication enhanced your relationships with co-workers, your supervisor and/or your employees at work?

____

____

____

2) How has your nonverbal communication hurt your relationships with co-workers, your supervisor and/or your employees at work?

____

____

____

3) How has your nonverbal communication been misinterpreted by co-workers, your supervisor and/or your employees at work?

____

____

____

4) Does the nonverbal communication you exhibit with co-workers, your supervisor and/or your employees show how you are truly feeling at the time?

____

____

____

Nonverbal Tips for Enhanced Communication

Following are some tips for enhancing your nonverbal communication when talking with other people. Remember that people from different cultures may show some variations of these behaviors.

- Always welcome people with a warm handshake.
- Find comfortable personal space when talking to another person. How close you get may depend on your relationship with the other person. The better you know someone, the closer you can stand when talking. Avoid being too close or too far away.
- Be relaxed and listen attentively to others. You can be a more effective listener and show positive attention by slightly leaning your body forward. This will show the other person that you are interested in the conversation.
- Maintain frequent eye contact. You should maintain a comfortable level of eye contact, but you should avoid staring, glaring or looking away.
- Provide nonverbal cues to the other person by nodding your head in approval.
- Keep gestures simple and unobtrusive.
- Stay alert when communicating with others. Closing your eyes, yawning or looking at your watch can block effective communication.
- Be aware of where you place your arms when talking. By crossing your arms across your chest, you will display a closed stance and appear not be open to what other people are saying.
- Make appropriate physical contact with other people. Be aware of when it is appropriate to hug, kiss and touch other people.
- Stand tall and straight; do not slouch.
- ______________________________
- ______________________________

Nonverbal Communication Identification

In the following table, look at the nonverbal communication in the left-hand column. In the right-hand column, write what you think the nonverbal communication means.

Nonverbal Communication	What does it mean?
Failing to maintain eye contact	
Standing erect, but not rigid	
Leaning slightly forward	
Tapping your fingers	
Nodding your head when listening	
Using your hands to gesture	
Clenching your fists	
Rolling your eyes	
Shaking hands warmly	
Crossed arms across chest	
Keep looking at your watch	
Yawning	

Nonverbal Communication Log

Think about a situation in which you would like to improve your nonverbal communication skills. This situation could be when speaking with a co-worker, your significant other, kids or the mail carrier. Complete the following log to learn more about your nonverbal communication:

Situation:____

With whom are you conversing:______________________________

His or her relationship to you:______________________________

What was your conversation about:____________________________

Are the messages you are speaking the same as what you are feeling? If not, why not?

Is the person someone with whom you really are interested in communicating? If it is not someone you are interested in, why do you?

(Continued on the next page)

(Nonverbal Communication Log continued)

Describe your body language.

What message is your body language giving?

How could you improve your body language?

What emotions does your body language hide?

Nonverbal Communication Pitfalls

What nonverbal communication pitfalls do find yourself in most often? Why?

Improving Nonverbals

How will you begin to improve your nonverbal communication when interacting with others?

Conversation and Nonverbals

How can you make sure that what you are saying matches your nonverbal communication?

Here are two examples of when someone's verbal communication does not match their nonverbal communication:

Angry, making fists and red in the face but continuing with a pleasant conversation.

Saying "I'm interested to know more" but looking around and watching the clock.

Improving Nonverbal Communication

- Awareness of nonverbal behavior will allow you to be a better receiver of messages
- You will learn to be a better sender of signals that reinforce understanding
- Nonverbal communication increases the degree of psychological closeness between people
- Learn about the nonverbal cues of people from different cultures

Nonverbal Communication

All of the following are aspects of nonverbal communication:

1) Eye contact
2) Facial expressions
3) Posture
4) Touch
5) Hand gestures
6) Proximity
7) Legs swinging
8) Finger tapping
9) Frequently looking away
10) Clenched fists

SECTION III:

Communication Skills Scale

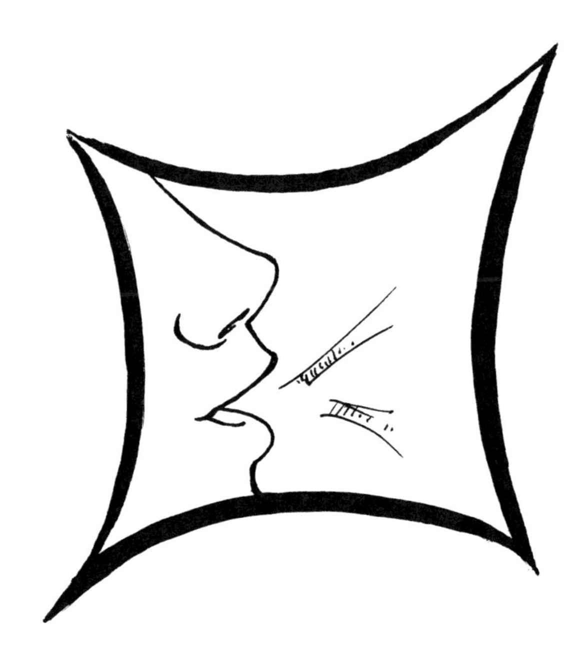

Name____

Date________________________

Communication Skills Scale Directions

The Communications Skills Scale can help you explore how effective you are when you are interacting with other people. This assessment contains 44 statements. Read each of the statements and decide how much you agree. In each of the choices listed, circle the number of your response on the line to the right of each statement. Ignore the number, just respond whether it is **Very True**, **Somewhat True** or **Not True**.

In the following example, the circled 1 indicates that the statement is not true of the person completing the scale:

	Very True	Somewhat True	Not True
1. I deliver clear messages to other people	3	2	(1)

This is not a test and there are no right or wrong answers. Do not spend too much time thinking about your answers. Your initial response will likely be the most true for you. Be sure to respond to every statement.

(Turn to the next page and begin)

Communication Skills Scale

	Very True	Somewhat True	Not True
1. I deliver clear messages to other people	3	2	1
2. When a conversation turns to feelings, I often change the subject	1	2	3
3. I am afraid to hurt the feelings of others	1	2	3
4. I am good at reading non-verbal messages	3	2	1
5. I know how to deliver messages that people can understand	3	2	1
6. I do not like to discuss sensitive issues	1	2	3
7. I am not afraid to express a differing opinion	3	2	1
8. I finish other peoples' sentences for them	1	2	3
9. People do not always get what I say to them	1	2	3
10. My emotions generally match my words	3	2	1
11. If I need to, I will stand up for myself	3	2	1
12. I let others speak without interrupting them	3	2	1
13. I am able to express my ideas clearly	3	2	1
14. I have trouble expressing my feelings	1	2	3
15. I am not as assertive as I could be	1	2	3
16. I ask questions when I do not understand	3	2	1
17. I have difficulty expressing my feelings	1	2	3
18. Often, I become angry when talking to others	1	2	3
19. I have trouble asking for what I want	1	2	3
20. I often pretend to listen, even though my mind wanders	1	2	3
21. I check to make sure people understand me	3	2	1
22. I can detect the emotional moods of others	3	2	1

(Continued on the next page)

(Communication Skills Scale continued)

	Very True	Somewhat True	Not True
23. I will express an opinion that is different from the group	3	2	1
24. I rarely jump to conclusions	3	2	1
25. I use "I" statements to deliver criticism to others	3	2	1
26. I get upset if others disagree with me	1	2	3
27. I do not like to anger others	1	2	3
28. I have trouble reading between the lines	1	2	3
29. I will ask for feedback about the messages I communicate	3	2	1
30. I often raise my voice, even though I am not aware of it at the time	1	2	3
31. I rarely ask questions so I will not look unintelligent	1	2	3
32. I always try to put myself in the speaker's shoes	3	2	1
33. I communicate nonverbally to match what I am saying	3	2	1
34. I try to avoid emotional situations	1	2	3
35. I am not hesitant to tell others how I feel	3	2	1
36. I get distracted easily	1	2	3
37. I often have to repeat what I say	1	2	3
38. I often change the subject when discussing touchy topics	1	2	3
39. I will not admit I am angry with someone	1	2	3
40. I am thinking about what I will say while people are talking to me	1	2	3
41. I only speak for myself, not everybody	3	2	1
42. I can solve problems without getting emotional	3	2	1
43. I cannot express my opinions if others do not share them	1	2	3
44. I listen to bits and pieces of most conversations	1	2	3

(Go to the Scoring Directions on the next page)

Communication Skills Scale
Scoring Directions

The Communications Skills Scale is designed to measure how well you are able to communicate with other people. Four important aspects of communicating effectively are:

- sending accurate messages
- controlling and discussing emotions
- being assertive when you need to and
- listening actively to what others are saying

These make up the four scales on the assessment. Scales are used to group items and help you to explore your specific communication skills more easily.

Scoring the assessment is very easy. Look at the questions you just answered.

Use the spaces below to record the number that you circled on each individual item of the assessment.

Then, calculate the totals for each of the columns (scales) and put that total underneath each column.

SCALE I	SCALE II	SCALE III	SCALE IV
1________	2________	3________	4________
5________	6________	7________	8________
9________	10________	11________	12________
13________	14________	15________	16________
17________	18________	19________	20________
21________	22________	23________	24________
25________	26________	27________	28________
29________	30________	31________	32________
33________	34________	35________	36________
37________	38________	39________	40________
41________	42________	43________	44________
I. Total	II. Total	III. Total	IV. Total
________	________	________	________
Messages	**Emotions**	**Assertiveness**	**Listening**

Profile Interpretation

Communication is the essence of social interaction and often determines how successful you are in your life and your career. Effective communication affects the impression you make on other people, the level of your self-esteem, your ability to manage situations and how you adjust socially in life. This assessment helps you explore how effective you are in four critical components of effective communication. Look at the profile interpretation materials below.

Individual Scale Score	Total Score All 4 Scales	Result	Indications
11 – 18	44 – 73	Low	You do not, at this point in time, have very effective communication skills. Think of different ways that you can develop and use communication skills more effectively.
19 – 25	74 – 102	Moderate	You have pretty good communication skills, but you could use some improvement. Think of ways to incorporate more effective communication skills into your conversations with other people.
26 – 33	103 – 132	High	You use effective communication skills a great deal of the time. Continue to use these effective communication skills when speaking with other people.

Regardless of your score on the Communications Skills Scale, low, moderate or high, you will benefit from doing all of the following exercises which have been designed to help you improve your communication skills.

I. Messages

Working on your communications skills will ensure that you send clear messages and that they are completely understood by other people. Miscommunication is the cause of many arguments and fights. Specific skills can be learned so others will understand your messages. To be more effective in communicating with others, remember the following:

- When sending messages, use words like I, me, and my to communicate your message. In this way, you own your messages that you share with other people. The use of words like they or some people are ineffective ways to communicate to others. Speak for yourself!
- Look at the person and speak to him or her directly. Do not repress your feelings. Unexpressed feelings have a tendency to blow up into larger conflicts.
- Express your feelings. See examples of how to express your feelings below. In the boxes on the left-hand side of the table, list people to whom you would like to express your feelings. In the right-hand column, express your feelings to that person.

Who I would like to express my feelings	What I would like to say to that person
My co-worker	*I feel angry when you don't pick me up on time for work.*
My spouse	*I get upset when you break your word.*

II. Emotions

In effective relationships, people are able to express themselves by sending emotional messages. This can be difficult because they force you to disclose personal information about yourself. This can be very risky. Complete the following statements to think about the emotional messages you would like to send to other people. List the person's name first and then complete the statement:

"____________________ , I get scared when you____

____

____

____"

"____________________ , I feel hurt when you____

____

____

____"

"____________________ , I feel unappreciated when you__________________________________

____

____

____"

"____________________ , I am sad when you____

____

____

____"

"____________________ , I get excited when you____

____

____

____"

III. Assertiveness

All people have the right to express their desires, needs and wants and expect other people to treat them with respect and dignity. AGGRESSIVE people will infringe on the rights of others and express their feelings through insults, sarcasm, hostile statements and put-downs. On the other hand, ASSERTIVE people describe their feelings and thoughts directly to other people in an honest way that enables them to act in their own best interest, allows them to stand up for themselves and exercise their personal rights without denying the rights of others. Assertive communication takes some practice. Complete the following statements:

Why do you have a hard time expressing your desires, needs and wants?

____

____

____

How has your aggressive style caused problems for you . . .

with your friends?

____

____

____

in your social life?

____

____

____

____

at work?

____

____

____

____

(Continued on the next page)

(Assertiveness continued)

How has your aggressive style caused problems for you . . .

with your finances?

with your family?

other ways?

What I Want

To assert yourself, you must know what you want in your life. By establishing what you really want, you will be able to assert yourself when you need to. You will know what is worth fighting for. You will also know from what to simply walk away.

In each of the boxes below, list what you want in each of the categories:

Personal	
Financial	
Career	
Family	
Friends	
Spirituality	
Community	
Other	

Non-Assertive Situations

Identify situations in which you need to be more assertive.

By becoming more aware of those situations in which you are not assertive, you can practice your assertiveness training skills.

For each of the situations listed below, describe how you show a lack of assertiveness.

Situations in which I lack assertiveness	**How I am non-assertive**
Saying NO to others	
Asking for favors	
Disagreeing with others' opinions	
Taking charge of a situation	
Social situations	
Responding to put-downs	
Stating my opinion	
Sexual situations	
Taking time for myself	
Speaking in front of groups	
Others (list them)	

People With Whom I Am Non-Assertive

Identify people with whom you need to be more assertive.

By becoming more aware of those people, you can practice your assertiveness training skills.

For each of the people listed below, describe how you show a lack of assertiveness.

People with whom I am non-assertive	How I am non-assertive
Mother	
Father	
Significant Other	
Co-Workers	
Children	
Sales Clerks	
Religious Leaders	
Authority Figures	
Neighbors	
Large Groups	
Supervisors	

IV. Listening

Active listening involves an awareness of what another person is saying to you or asking you to do.

Use your active listening skills to make sure that you understand the true meaning of the request or statement. Following are some of the blocks to listening:

INADEQUATE LISTENING – It is easy to get distracted when other people are talking. This includes such things as being too involved with your own thoughts, preoccupied with your own needs and problems or too eager to help the other person. It might be that the social and cultural differences between you and the other person are too great.

List times when you feel you easily get distracted when talking with others:

____

____

____

To what specific people do you find it hard to listen?

____

____

____

JUDGMENTAL LISTENING – Listening with the intent of judging a person can hinder your ability to listen to them. You may find that you are judging what the person is saying as good or bad, right or wrong; you are not listening with empathy. It is important to set aside your judgments about the person until you can better understand him or her, his or her world and point of view.

List times when you feel you start to value-judge the other person:

____

____

____

What specific people do find yourself evaluating?

____

____

____

(Continued on the next page)

(Listening continued)

DAYDREAMING – Everyone's attention will wander from time to time. If you find yourself having a hard time listening to someone, it is probably a sign that you are avoiding or are uninterested in the person or certain topics of conversation.

List times when you feel your attention wandering:

____

____

____

When your mind wanders, which specific people are you talking to? Why does it happen?

____

____

____

REHEARSING – Any time you ask yourself the question "How should I respond to what this person is saying?" you distract yourself from what the person says. As you get better at active listening, your response just comes naturally. It is best to listen intently to the person, the themes, and core messages related to their words. Then allow your intuition to provide you with a response.

List times when you find yourself rehearsing what you will say in conversations:

____

____

____

Which specific people are you talking with when you find yourself rehearsing your conversation?

____

____

____

I Need to Improve

Which communication skills do you need most to improve?
How will you do that?

Messages:____________________

Emotions:____________________

Assertiveness:____________________

Listening:____________________

Being More Assertive

How are you going to be more assertive?
With which people and in what situations?

Messages:____

Emotions:____

Assertiveness:____

Listening:____

Clear Messages

How will you ensure that people get clear messages from you and that you truly listen to what others are saying?

Communication Pitfalls

- Expecting other people to read your mind
- Sending mixed messages
- Being sarcastic
- Jumping from topic to topic
- Accusing others
- Dragging up the past
- Disclosing too much information about yourself

Rewards of Effective Communication

- Mutual understanding
- Less chance of conflict
- Cooperation from others
- Meeting another's needs while getting your own needs met
- Relief from negative emotions such as guilt, jealousy and anger
- Enhanced closeness

SECTION IV:

Social Radar Scale

Name____

Date__________________________

Social Radar Scale Directions

Social Radar is at the heart of every relationship. It is the ability to see through social and racial myths, accept and value people who are different from you, and understand and recognize subtle nuances between what other people are saying and what they are feeling.

The Social Radar Scale can help you identify how effectively you are able to develop a rapport with people with whom you have a relationship. This scale contains 36 statements. Read each of the statements and decide if the statement is like you or not like you. In each of the choices listed, circle your response on the line to the right of each statement.

In the following example, the circled **Like Me** indicates that the statement describes the person taking the assessment:

SECTION 1: VALUING DIVERSITY

I recognize the importance of diversity among people

Not Like Me

This is not a test and there are no right or wrong answers. Do not spend too much time thinking about your answers. Your initial response will likely be the most true for you. Be sure to respond to every statement.

(Turn to the next page and begin)

Social Radar Scale

SECTION I: VALUING DIVERSITY

1.	I recognize the importance of diversity among people	Like Me	Not Like Me
2.	I value diversity as a valuable resource	Like Me	Not Like Me
3.	I enjoy being with people who are different from me	Like Me	Not Like Me
4.	I am tolerant of differences in people	Like Me	Not Like Me
5.	I work well with people who are different from me	Like Me	Not Like Me
6.	I enjoy helping people who are different from me	Like Me	Not Like Me
7,	I am proud of my historical and cultural heritage	Like Me	Not Like Me
8.	I work constantly to reduce my prejudices when interacting with people different from me	Like Me	Not Like Me
9.	I rarely stereotype other people or cultures	Like Me	Not Like Me
10.	I believe that diversity is necessary in life	Like Me	Not Like Me
11.	I can work with people different from me to achieve mutual goals	Like Me	Not Like Me
12.	I believe in the equal worth of all people	Like Me	Not Like Me

(Continued on the next page)

(Social Radar Scale continued)

SECTION II: INTUITIVENESS

1.	I get hunches about things that are happening in my life	Like Me	Not Like Me
2.	I am able to easily sense what other people are feeling	Like Me	Not Like Me
3.	I sometimes know about events before they happen	Like Me	Not Like Me
4.	I sometimes am able to feel physical sensations that alert me when something is wrong	Like Me	Not Like Me
5.	I make many decisions based on hunches	Like Me	Not Like Me
6.	I am aware of times when my intuition speaks to me	Like Me	Not Like Me
7.	I am sometimes able to predict what will happen in the future	Like Me	Not Like Me
8.	I often receive intuitive information through physical sensations such as a knot in my stomach or the hair standing up on my neck	Like Me	Not Like Me
9.	I often know things but do not know how I know them	Like Me	Not Like Me
10.	I often receive sudden flashes of insight (aha moments)	Like Me	Not Like Me
11.	I often feel a sudden rush of understanding	Like Me	Not Like Me
12.	I often feel like I have done something before	Like Me	Not Like Me

(Continued on the next page)

(The Social Radar Scale continued)

SECTION III: EMPATHY

1.	I help the person to identify the feelings that are being experienced	Like Me	Not Like Me
2.	I am attuned to what the person may be only half saying	Like Me	Not Like Me
3.	I am attuned to what the person may be hinting at	Like Me	Not Like Me
4.	I am attuned to what the hidden message is behind what is said	Like Me	Not Like Me
5.	I usually attempt to read the intensity of the other person's emotions	Like Me	Not Like Me
6.	I am aware of the person's body language	Like Me	Not Like Me
7.	I am aware of my own bodily reactions during the conversation	Like Me	Not Like Me
8.	I often help people tell their stories	Like Me	Not Like Me
9.	I bond very quickly with most people	Like Me	Not Like Me
10.	I am good at sensing other people's perspectives	Like Me	Not Like Me
11.	I often paraphrase back to the person what I heard	Like Me	Not Like Me
12.	I can experience the person's world as if I were the other person	Like Me	Not Like Me

(Go to the Scoring Directions on the next page)

Social Radar Scale
Scoring Directions

The Social Radar Scale is designed to measure your capacity to understand what is happening in your relationships and then help you to respond to that understanding in a personal and socially-effective manner. People who possess this social radar know how to value diversity, are intuitive, and show a great deal of empathy.

These characteristics are prominent and make up the three scales for the assessment. To score the assessment:

1. Add the number of **Like Me** responses you circled in each of the three previous sections.
2. Then, transfer your totals for each of the three sections to the corresponding lines below:
3. Total all three sections.

Section I: Valuing Diversity Total = _______

Section II: Intuitiveness Total = _______

Section III: Empathy Total = _______

Section I, II and III TOTAL = _______

Social Radar Scale
Profile Interpretation

Individual Scale's Score	Total Score All 4 Scales	Result	Indications
9 – 12	25 – 36	High	You have the beliefs and behaviors of someone who has a great deal of social radar. You are able to work and live effectively with people who are different from you, you have developed your intuitive powers and you show a great deal of empathy for other people.
4 – 8	13 – 24	Moderate	You have developed some of the beliefs and behaviors of someone who has a great deal of social radar. You are able to work and live effectively with people who are different from you, you have developed some intuitive powers and you show empathy for other people. You still have a little work to do.
0 – 3	0 – 12	Low	You do not have the beliefs and behaviors of someone who has social radar. You possibly are not able to work and live effectively with people who are different from you, you probably have not developed your intuitive powers and you might not show much empathy for other people. You need to work to develop skills to be more effective in your interpersonal relationships.

For scales which you scored in the Moderate or Low range, find the descriptions on the pages that follow. Read the description and complete the exercises that are included. No matter how you scored, low, moderate or high, you will benefit from all of these exercises.

Social Radar Scale Descriptions

Scale I: VALUING DIVERSITY

People scoring High on this scale understand the importance of living, and working with a variety of different people. They value diversity as a resource and enjoy the benefits that diversity brings. When communicating with other people, they are tolerant of differences in people and can work cooperatively with people from diverse backgrounds. They are proud of their cultural background and enjoy the pride others show in their cultural background. They work to reduce any prejudices they have and tend not to stereotype people from other cultures. They truly believe that all people are equal.

Scale II: INTUITIVENESS

People scoring High on this scale tend to be very intuitive about things and people. When communicating with other people, they can very easily sense what people are feeling and will use these insights to quickly and easily develop rapport. They often feel sudden flashes of understanding and use these flashes to enhance their ability to communicate with other people. They know things without having to think about them.

Scale III: EMPATHY

People scoring High on this scale are uniquely attuned to other people. They can easily understand what people are feeling, and the intensity of those feelings. When communicating with other people, they bond very quickly. They are attuned to the hidden messages behind what people are saying, and can easily put themselves into the shoes of others. They can easily read between the lines of a normal conversation. They can sense the perspective of others and can experience their world as if they were that person.

People with high social radar are socially intelligent and tend to have effective interpersonal relationships. They tend to quickly and easily understand what other people are trying to say, are very intuitive and good at reading between the lines of a conversation, and have developed genuine feelings of compassion and regard for their fellow human beings.

Regardless of your scores on the assessment, you can increase your social radar by completing all of the exercises that follow.

Valuing Diversity

We live in a very complex society. Interacting effectively with people from different cultures, ethnic groups, socio-economic classes, races and historical backgrounds is critical. Often, interacting with people different from us does not come naturally. The process of valuing diversity is important because we will be required to communicate effectively with people despite the natural barriers of culture, religion, work ethic, gender, race and social class. In addition, we will inevitably see greater diversity among our friends, teachers, classmates, co-workers, neighbors and people in our community. Therefore, we must be skilled in relating to various individuals.

My Friends

To learn more about the diversity of the people with whom you are friends, complete the following table:

My friends who are different from me	**How these friends are different** (race, social status, religion, gender, culture, etc.)
Jane	*Jane was born in Russia.*

My Diverse Friends

In the table that follows list some of the things you like about your diverse friends.

My friends who are different from me	What I enjoy about this person
Jane	*She is so interesting. She speaks another language with her family. Their foods are different than ours and are delicious. They have different customs than I do.*

Who Am I?

It is important that you develop an awareness and an appreciation for who you are.

Complete the following table to better appreciate your own cultural heritage.

Describe your cultural backround.	
Describe your social class identity.	
Describe your ethnic identity (sense of belonging to one ethic group).	
Describe your religious background.	

Intuition

Intuition is difficult to define. The word intuition actually comes from the Latin root meaning to look within. Many times we are in a conversation with another person and have difficulty quieting our own mind. This internal chatter helps the logical mind to continue operating, thus keeping your intuitive mind from emerging. With practice, however, you will find it much easier to turn off the chatter from the logical part of your brain. To be as intuitive as possible you will need to learn to become more attuned to your inner intuitive mind. To begin the process of learning to access your intuitive mind, you first have to quiet your logical mind. As the dominant logical mind begins to quiet, the intuitive mind begins to emerge and become available to you.

EXPERIENTIAL EXERCISE

Try the following exercise to see how easy it is for you to quiet your logical mind. Sit still for several minutes and try to quiet your logical mind. Close your eyes and stop the internal chatter going on in your mind. Let go or block out any interfering thoughts, anxieties or emotions that pop into your head. After several minutes open your eyes and answer the following questions:

How difficult was it to quiet your logical mind and why?

____

____

____

____

What thoughts and emotions kept popping into your head?

____

____

____

____

(Intuition continued)

AFFIRMATIONS

Probably the best tool for you to use in quieting your logical mind is the use of affirmations. Affirmations are phrases you can use to reprogram your mind. They are brief statements that put you in the proper frame of mind to accept intuitive inputs. Affirmations are a way of sending your brain a message that the desired result has already been achieved. What you state, in the present tense, can easily be achieved. Examples of affirmation that might be used in helping to accept intuitive inputs include:

"My intuitive ability grows stronger with each counseling session."

"My intuitive signals get stronger and clearer as I speak with different people."

"My intuition is available and accessible to me during counseling sessions."

"My intuition is increasingly strengthened as I complete the exercises in this workbook."

EXPERIENTIAL EXERCISE

Using the examples of affirmations above, formulate some of your own affirmations below:

____

____

____

____

____

____

____

____

(Continued on the next page)

(Intuition continued)

WORD CONCENTRATION

Another way to quiet your logical mind is by concentrating on a word – in this case the word INTUITION. By focusing your attention on the word INTUITION and what it means to you, you can jump-start the intuition development process.

Follow the instructions below:

Relax your body.

Sit quietly and simply hold the word INTUITION in your awareness.

Visualize the word spelled out before you.

Concentrate on the word INTUITION.

As other thoughts attempt to intrude on your concentration, simply refocus your full attention to the word INTUITION.

If you feel your attention wandering, bring it back to the word INTUITION in your awareness.

As word symbols and associations appear in your awareness, you may want to make a note of them in your workbook.

Do this for five minutes. Attempt to increase the time you attend to this word.

After you have completed this experiential exercise, complete the following questions:

How hard was it for you to hold the word INTUITION in your mind? Why was that?

____

____

____

Did other thoughts keep you from total concentration on the word? If so, explain how.

____

____

____

(Intuition continued)

FREE ASSOCIATION

Associations are also a way of quieting your logical mind through full concentration. Free association is a technique which allows you to generate words and ideas without judging them. Free association will allow you to bypass your logical mind and allow your intuitive mind to surface.

Follow the instructions below:

Start by writing down the word INTUITION

Let your mind go and allow it to freely associate.

Write associations that you have with the word INTUITION.

Next to the word, write a word that you associate with intuition.

Then write the word INTUITION again and write another word that you associate with intuition.

Continue this process until you have written twenty-five or more words that you associate with intuition. If you cannot think of any words, write the word "FREE" in the space next to the word INTUITION and continue.

Continue to write your associations even if you repeat some of them.

For example: Intuition . . . Feeling . . . Intuition . . . Word . . . Intuition . . . Free . . .

Intuition . . . Growth . . . Intuition . . . Mind . . . Intuition . . . Right-brain . . .

Now you try it!

____

____

____

____

____

____

Empathy

Empathy is at the very heart of all conversations you have with other people. Empathic listening, however, is not as easy as it sounds. Empathic listening involves using all of your intuitive powers to help you be able to perceive the other person's internal frame of reference. The problem is that many different things can interfere with your ability to actively listen to other people during a conversation.

PREPARATION FOR EMPATHIC LISTENING

Empathic listening is a skill that develops over time. The next section helps you develop the intuitive skills necessary for developing advanced empathy. The following table will describe some ways for you to listen more empathically.

In your next conversation with someone, use the empathic behaviors listed in the left-hand column. Then, in the right-hand column, write about how you felt using this behavior:

Empathic behavior	How you felt using this behavior
Pay attention, both physically and psychologically, and listen to the person's point of view.	
Try to set your judgments and biases aside for the moment and walk in the shoes of the person.	
As the person speaks, listen especially for the messages behind the words.	
Listen to both the verbal and nonverbal messages and their context.	
Respond fairly frequently, but briefly, to the person's actual messages.	
Move gradually toward the exploration of sensitive topics and feelings.	
After responding with empathy, pay attention to cues that either confirm or deny the accuracy of your response.	

Social Radar – Not!

Write about how you have not shown good social radar when communicating with others.

Enhancing Social Radar

What has surprised you about completing some of the exercises used to enhance social radar?

Developing Social Radar

What will you do now, or in the future, to further develop your social radar?

What Is Intuition?

Some of the definitions that have been proposed for intuition include:

- A way of knowing what to do without thinking
- The ability to make decisions without the use of logic
- Hunches
- Gut feelings about decisions which go against logic
- Knowing something without conscious awareness
- Knowing something through the subconscious, rather than a logical analysis
- Knowing without knowing why
- Random thoughts
- Knowing without logical or rational thought
- A premonition
- Insights
- A sixth sense
- Vision

How People Receive Intuitive Input

- **Physical Knowing (Body)** – Examples of physical intuitive cues might include physical sensations such as a gut feeling about something; a stomachache or butterflies in your stomach; ringing in your ears; hair standing up on the back of your neck; a tension headache; a bad taste in your mouth.

- **Clear Seeing (Mind)** – Examples of visual intuitive cues might include Aha feelings; a light bulb being turned on in your mind; instant illumination about a topic; seeing the light; or a sudden rush of understanding.

- **Clear Knowing (Emotional)** – Examples of emotional intuitive cues might include sudden feelings about something; an instant like or dislike for someone or something; feeling like you have met someone before; feeling like you have done something before; sudden changes in mood or affect; feelings of unconditional receptivity to someone without knowing why.

- **Clear Hearing (Auditory)** – Examples of auditory intuitive cues include listening to the little voice in your head; hearing bells ringing; hearing music; hearing voices; or insightful thinking.

- **Spiritual Knowing (Soul)** – Examples of spiritual intuitive cues might include mystical experiences; a sudden understanding of yourself and others; a feeling of creativity when facing a problem; a feeling of connection with someone or something greater than you; or a sense of true purpose in life.

SECTION V:

Negotiation Process-Style Scale

Name____

Date______________________

Negotiation Process-Style Scale Directions

Disagreements are a natural part of any relationship. Negotiation is a special skill from which everyone benefits. Your ability to negotiate will allow you to get what you want without alienating or manipulating others, possibly by compromise, and reach a mutually agreeable solution.

The Negotiation Process-Style Scale is designed to help you understand more about the type of negotiator you are, and will provide you with insights into the negotiation styles of people with whom you have relationships.

This booklet contains 28 statements that are divided into four negotiation process styles. Read each statement and decide the extent to which the statement describes you.

Circle 3 if the statement is **A Lot Like Me**

Circle 2 if the statement is **A Little Like Me**

Circle 1 if the statement is **Not Like Me**

In the negotiating process with another person,

I prefer to talk about issues 3 (2) 1

In the above statement, the circled 2 means that the statement is **A Little Like** the person completing the scale. Ignore the TOTAL lines below each section. They are for scoring purposes and will be used later.

This is not a test and there are no right or wrong answers. Do not spend too much time thinking about your answers. Your initial response will likely be the most true for you. Be sure to respond to every statement.

(Turn to the next page and begin)

Negotiation Process-Style Scale

3 = A Lot Like Me **2 = A Little Like Me** **1 = Not Like Me**

Section I:
In the negotiating process with another person,

1.	I prefer to talk about issues	3	2	1
2.	I rely on my highly developed verbal persuasion skills	3	2	1
3.	I like to talk more then listen	3	2	1
4.	I am influenced by how I feel	3	2	1
5.	I rely on gut feelings rather than logic	3	2	1
6.	I skip from topic to topic often	3	2	1
7.	I get bored quickly with too much detail	3	2	1

I - TOTAL = _________

3 = A Lot Like Me **2 = A Little Like Me** **1 = Not Like Me**

Section II:
In the negotiating process with another person,

1.	I use a lot of facts and logic	3	2	1
2.	I can become aggressive if I need to	3	2	1
3.	I have clear goals about what I want	3	2	1
4.	I use detail and process to my advantage	3	2	1
5.	I stay focused as long as it serves my end result	3	2	1
6.	I value details as long as they are pertinent	3	2	1
7.	I see negotiation as a game to win	3	2	1

II - TOTAL = _________

(Continued on the next page)

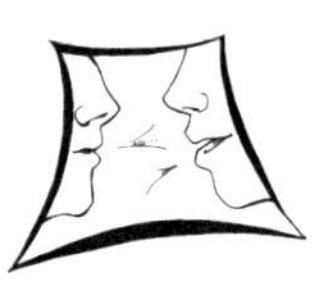

(Negotiation Process-Style Scale continued)

3 = A Lot Like Me **2 = A Little Like Me** **1 = Not Like Me**

Section III:
In the negotiating process with another person,

1.	I can be very intimidating	3	2	1
2.	I believe that being prepared is the key to negotiating	3	2	1
3.	I am prepared to defend my beliefs	3	2	1
4.	I am good at listening and sizing others up	3	2	1
5.	I stay on track	3	2	1
6.	I am able to back up my beliefs	3	2	1
7.	I want to get to the bottom line as quickly as possible	3	2	1

III - TOTAL = ________

3 = A Lot Like Me **2 = A Little Like Me** **1 = Not Like Me**

Section IV:
In the negotiating process with another person,

1.	I am guided by my emotions	3	2	1
2.	I will defer to others for assistance	3	2	1
3.	I prefer to listen to the other person	3	2	1
4.	I am not comfortable talking through the process	3	2	1
5.	I am interested in smallest details	3	2	1
6.	I will negotiate based on my value system	3	2	1
7.	I am more concerned about the process rather than winning	3	2	1

IV - TOTAL = ________

(Go to the Scoring Directions on the next page)

Negotiation Process-Style Scale Scoring Directions

The Negotiating Process-Style Scale is designed to measure the style you use when you are negotiating with other people. Total the numbers you've circled for each of the four sections on the previous pages. Put that total on the line marked TOTAL at the end of each section.

Then, transfer your totals for each of the four sections to the lines below and total the four sections:

SECTION I	TALKER	TOTAL = ________
SECTION II	AGGRESSOR	TOTAL = ________
SECTION III	PREPARER	TOTAL = ________
SECTION IV	LISTENER	TOTAL = ________
ALL FOUR SECTIONS		TOTAL = ________

Profile Interpretation

Individual Scale Score	Total Score All 4 Scales	Result	Indications
17 – 21	66 – 84	High	In the negotiation process, you tend to incorporate and use many of the characteristics of this negotiation process style.
12 – 16	47 – 65	Moderate	In the negotiation process, you tend to incorporate and use some of the characteristics of this negotiation process style.
7 – 11	28 – 46	Low	In the negotiation process, you tend to incorporate and use very few of the characteristics of this negotiation process style.

Conflict arises when two people have different opinions about an issue or issues. There is no one best style to use in all situations in which you are negotiating. Each of the styles can be useful in different situations. You do not have a single specific style for dealing with all negotiations. People are able to use all four styles. Many of us, however, rely on and get comfortable using one of the styles more often than the others. The area in which you scored the highest tends to be the negotiation style you use most often. Similarly, the area in which you scored the lowest tends to be your least used negotiation style. To learn more about why you prefer one style more than the others, turn to the next page for a description of each of the four styles on the assessment. Please answer the questions related to each of the styles.

Negotiation Process-Style Profile Interpretation

SCALE I — TALKER: People with a Talker Negotiation Process Style prefer to talk through the negotiation process and to dictate the pace of the process. They prefer to talk rather than listen, and they rely on their conversational skills to try to control the negotiating process. They tend to rely more on emotions and gut feelings than on logic and analysis. In the end, they need to feel good about the end results.

List times when this negotiating style has worked well for you.

____

____

____

____

____

List times when this negotiating style has not worked well for you.

____

____

____

____

____

Compare and contrast situations in which your style has and has not worked well.
What patterns do you notice?

____

____

____

____

____

(Continued on the next page)

(Negotiation Process-Style Profile Interpretation continued)

SCALE II — AGGRESSOR: People with an Aggressor Negotiating Process Style rely on facts and logic to accomplish their purpose and meet their needs. They have clear goals and tend to try to steam roll others with little regard to emotions. They can become aggressive if pushed in the negotiation process. They are primarily concerned about succeeding in getting what they want out of the negotiation process. They like to be in control of the process and will do what they need to in order to win.

List times when this negotiation style has worked well for you.

____

____

____

____

____

List times when this negotiation style has not worked well for you.

____

____

____

____

____

Compare and contrast situations in which your style has and has not worked well.
What patterns do you notice?

____

____

____

____

____

(Continued on the next page)

(Negotiation Process-Style Profile Interpretation continued)

SCALE III — PREPARER: People with a Preparer Negotiation Process Style believe that proof of what is right will often determine the outcome of the negotiation. They believe that if you cannot prove your point logically, then why even negotiate. They have little need for emotions and feel that emotions play no part in the negotiation process. They like to be prepared and believe that the best prepared people win in the negotiation process.

List times when this negotiation style has worked well for you.

____

____

____

____

____

List times when this negotiation style has not worked well for you.

____

____

____

____

____

Compare and contrast situations in which your style has and has not worked well. What patterns do you notice?

____

____

____

____

____

(Continued on the next page)

(Negotiation Process-Style Profile Interpretation continued)

SCALE IV — LISTENER: People with a Listener Negotiation Process Style usually prefer listening to talking or arguing. They will gladly accept assistance from other people during the process because they do not enjoy the negotiation process. They are guided by their value system, and the process is often more important to them than the end results. They respect the rules of the negotiating process and desire win-win end results.

List times when this negotiating style has worked well for you.

List times when this negotiating style has not worked well for you.

Compare and contrast situations in which your style has and has not worked well.
What patterns do you notice?

NEGOTIATION SITUATIONS

It is important to identify and understand the situations which require you to begin the negotiation process in your life. The next two exercises will help you learn more about where and when you negotiate the most.

Where My Negotiations Occur

List where and with whom most of your negotiations occur (see example in the first set of boxes).

Where they occur	With whom they occur
In my home	My significant other

When My Negotiations Occur

List when most of your negotiations occur and what you dislike about the situation that causes you to feel uncomfortable.

When they occur	What I dislike about the situation
During a sporting event	I want to concentrate on the game, not have a serious conversation

Negotiation Process Worksheet

Identify a major negotiation that you have been involved in during the past year. This could have been with your parents, brother, sister, peer, significant other, co-worker, supervisor or teacher.

Negotiation Situation: ______________________________

____

____

____

1. What strategy or negotiation process style did you use?

____

____

____

____

2. What did you want? What did the other person want?

____

____

____

____

3. What was the result of the negotiation?

____

____

____

____

4. What strategies did you use to bring the resolution to a conclusion?

____

____

____

____

Negotiation Patterns

List five negotiations that you can remember throughout your life.
What strategies did you use and how effective were the results?

Negotiations	What were the negotiations results?

Ideal Negotiations

1) Conflict and disagreement is inevitable.

List a negotiation situation that you are facing:

2) Getting angry and frustrated will not help.

How can you avoid getting upset and angry in the situation?

3) Individual people or groups have different interests or agendas.

Who are the individual people or groups involved in your negotiation?

4) Separate feelings from the agenda.

How can you do this?

(Ideal Negotiations continued)

5) Focus on outcomes, not positions.

What are the desired outcomes of this negotiation?

6) Identify mutually agreeable solutions.

What is the ultimate solution you would like to see?

7) Be flexible.

How can you remain flexible during the negotiation process?

8) Come to an agreement.

How can you and the other party come to some sort of agreement?

Being a Better Negotiator

Write about what you can start doing today to become a better negotiator.

My Recent Negotiations

Write about some negotiations you have recently been a part of, and how the knowledge you gained from this assessment could have been helpful to you.

Learned Attributes of Negotiations

Describe some of the attributes of the other negotiation types that you would like to possess and why.

Principles of Successful Negotiation

- Conflict and disagreement is inevitable
- Getting angry and frustrated will not help
- Individual people or groups have different interests or agendas
- Separate your own feelings from the agenda
- Focus on outcomes, not positions
- Identify mutually agreeable solutions
- Be flexible
- Come to an agreement

Four Negotiation Styles

SCALE I — TALKER

People with a Talker Negotiation-Process Style prefer to talk through the negotiation process and to dictate the pace of the process. They prefer to talk rather than listen, and they rely on their conversational skills to try to control the negotiating process.

SCALE II — AGGRESSOR

People with an Aggressor Negotiating-Process Style rely on facts and logic to accomplish their purpose and meet their needs. They have clear goals and tend to try to "steam roll" others with little regard to emotions.

SCALE III — PREPARER

People with a Preparer Negotiation-Process Style believe that proof of what is right will often determine the outcome of the negotiation. They believe that if you cannot prove your point logically, then why even negotiate.

SCALE IV — LISTENER

People with a Listener Negotiation-Process Style usually prefer listening to talking or arguing. They will gladly accept assistance from other people during the process because they do not enjoy the negotiation process.